Puzzle #1

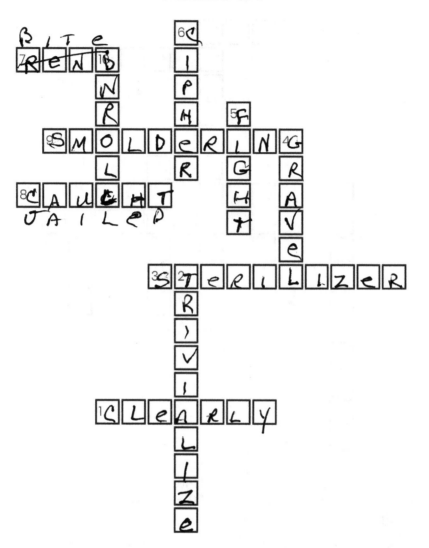

Across

[1] without doubt or question

[3] a device for heating substances above their boiling point

[7] to grip, cut off, or tear with or as if with the teeth or jaws

[8] being in captivity

[9] showing scarcely suppressed anger

Down

[2] make insignificant

[4] rock fragments and pebbles

[5] be engaged in a contest or struggle

[6] a secret method of writing

[10] register formally as a participant or member

Puzzle #2

Across

[2] a brief description given for purposes of identification

[5] a club used for hitting a ball in various games

[6] look at and say out loud something written or printed

[7] branch of medicine concerned with the treatment of children

Down

[1] the branch of medicine that deals with diseases of the blood

[3] inflict an emotional wound or shock upon

[4] transform by heating

[8] the time yet to come

[9] exchange or deliver for money or its equivalent

Puzzle #3

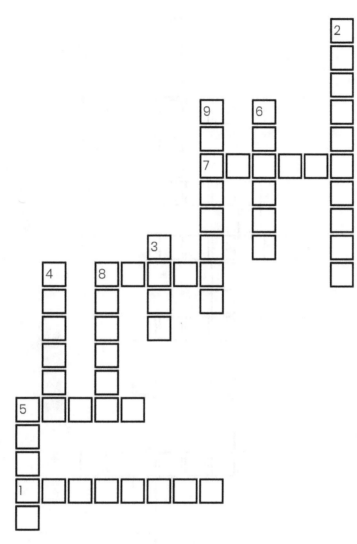

Across
[1] a means of communicating by the use of sounds or symbols

[5] take something or somebody with oneself somewhere

[7] take something away as by lifting, pushing, or taking off

[8] the faculty through which the external world is apprehended

Down
[2] combine and form a complex whole

[3] be cognizant or aware of a fact or a piece of information

[4] feelings of great warmth and intensity

[5] make by combining materials and parts

[6] having few parts

[8] a tube used to move liquid from one vessel to another

[9] being everywhere equidistant

Puzzle #4

Across

[1] domination to the exclusion of others

[2] of or relating to behavior

Down

[3] the adoption of the behavior of the surrounding culture

[4] a wild and exciting undertaking

Puzzle #5

Across

[3] occurring in or belonging to the present time

[4] change of position that does not entail a change of location

Down

[1] the condition of someone who knows and comprehends

[2] the faculty that enables us to distinguish scents

Puzzle #6

Across
[1] in line with a length or direction

[2] small or little relative to something else

[5] being in harmony with your taste or likings

[6] cause to concentrate about two conflicting positions

Down
[3] an ability that has been acquired by training

[4] derive or receive pleasure from

[5] subject to propaganda

[8] resisting weight or pressure

[9] the act of raising to the highest possible point

Puzzle #7

Across

[1] the act of increasing the prestige or power of something

[3] keep from happening or arising

[8] construct a hypothesis about

[10] keep or maintain in unaltered condition

[11] the mother of Jesus

Down

[2] a quality of spirit that enables you to face danger or pain

[3] cause to run

[4] a hard black form of lignite that takes a brilliant polish

[5] underground plant organ that lacks buds or leaves or nodes

[6] an artifact designed to be played with

[7] conforming to a standard or pattern

Puzzle #8

Across
[1] marked by continuous modification or effective action

[2] drawn toward a center or brought under the control of a central authority

[6] provide with additional fuel, as of aircraft, ships, and cars

[7] adaptation to a new climate

[9] bring forth or yield

Down
[3] exercising caution or showing attention

[4] obtain

[5] the imposition of a new organization

[8] having the properties of a magnet

[9] on the positive side or higher end of a scale

[10] a Christian missionary to the Gentiles

Puzzle #9

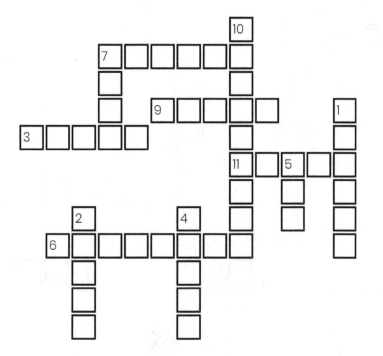

Across

[3] emit light

[6] arrange by systematic planning and united effort

[7] the warmest season of the year

[9] food and lodging provided in addition to money

[11] of or belonging to or characteristic of a particular area

Down

[1] a long depression in the surface of the land

[2] an implement that has hairs or bristles set into a handle

[4] the cardinal number that is the product of ten and five

[5] a tight-fitting headdress

[7] a natural protective body covering and site of the sense of touch

[10] supply with battlements

Puzzle #10

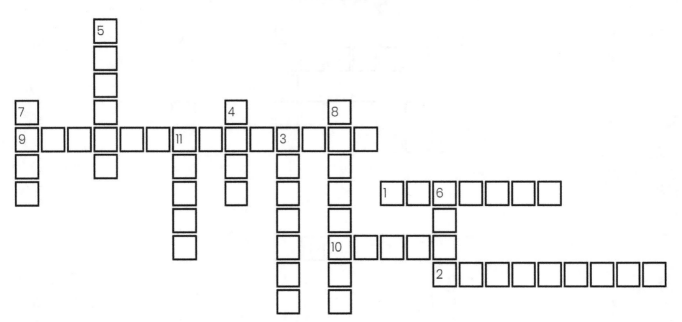

Across

[1] having the same or nearly the same characteristics

[2] of or related to or containing sulfur or derived from sulfur

[9] made for or adjusted to a particular person

[10] machine that creates mechanical energy and imparts movement

Down

[3] have as a part

[4] tool for exerting pressure or lifting

[5] a thin cylindrical pointed writing implement

[6] Roman god of war and agriculture

[7] sit and travel on the back of animal, usually while controlling its motions

[8] disease characterized by overproduction of white blood cells

[11] the extent downward or backward or inward

Puzzle #11

Across

[1] a lump or mass of hard consolidated mineral matter

[3] many times at short intervals

[4] write in large alphabetic characters

[5] a three-sided polygon

[8] a division of a stem arising from the main stem of a plant

[9] the process of abstracting common properties of instances

Down

[2] an itemized statement of money owed for goods or services

[6] a methodical and orderly manner or approach

[7] a person who is able to write and has written something

[10] come to pass

[11] to consider or examine in speech or writing

Puzzle #12

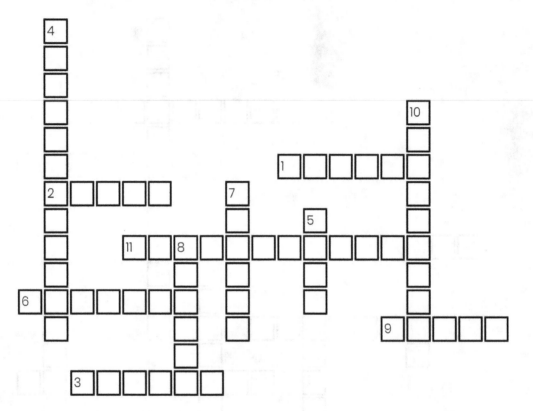

Across

[1] have an influence upon

[2] present for acceptance or rejection

[3] in truth (often tends to intensify)

[6] someone in the business of selling jewelry

[9] of comparatively great physical weight or density

[11] the sound made by the vibration of vocal folds modified by the resonance of the vocal tract

Down

[4] having sections or patches colored differently and usually brightly

[5] perform or carry out

[7] the official home of a king, queen, or other exalted person

[8] ellipse in which the two axes are of equal length

[10] provide support for

Puzzle #13

Across

[1] mechanical vibrations transmitted by an elastic medium

[2] use language

[5] having little length or lacking in length

[7] diameter of a tube or gun barrel

[11] bring something new to an environment

Down

[3] a rigid piece of metal or wood

[4] possession of the qualities required to do something

[6] having a surface without slope

[8] an untroubled state that is free from disturbances

[9] a basic unit of length (approximately 1.094 yards)

[10] produced or marked by conscious design or premeditation

Puzzle #14

Across

[4] have an end, in a temporal, spatial, or quantitative sense

[5] be specific about

[10] draw air into, and expel out of, the lungs

Down

[1] the characteristics by which a thing or person is known

[2] the act of putting something in a certain place

[3] an unshaved growth of hair on the upper lip

[6] where people and merchandise can enter or leave a country

[7] an enclosure in which animals can be kept

[8] posing no difficulty

[9] free from error

[11] quantifier

Puzzle #15

Across
[1] narrow-leaved green herbage: grown as lawns

[3] free from impurities

[4] water-soluble pigment

[9] the armed forces of a nation

[11] an outer garment that covers the body from shoulder down

Down
[2] the profession devoted to alleviating diseases and injuries

[5] perceive with attention

[6] move obliquely or sideways, usually in an uncontrolled manner

[7] give money, usually in exchange for goods or services

[8] move around an axis or a center

[10] utter aloud, often with surprise, horror, or joy

Puzzle #16

Across
[2] a line of text indicating what the passage below it is about

[3] precipitation falling from clouds in the form of ice crystals

[5] feline mammal usually having thick soft fur

[6] a string of words satisfying grammatical rules of a language

[8] the first month of the year

Down
[1] a logical motive for a belief or action

[2] a male partner in a marriage

[3] a kitchen appliance used for cooking food

[5] enjoying or affording comforting warmth and shelter

[7] take without referencing from someone's writing or speech

Puzzle #17

Across
[1] informal or slang terms for mentally irregular

[4] make optimal

[7] be in charge of, act on, or dispose of

[9] edge tool used as a cutting instrument

[11] a military officer of highest rank

Down
[2] a celebrant who shares in a noisy party

[3] displaying or setting off to best advantage

[5] heat food in order to kill harmful microorganisms

[6] lower and raise the head, as to indicate assent or agreement or confirmation

[8] people in general (often used in the plural)

Puzzle #18

Across

[1] showing or causing joy and pleasure

[2] uninterrupted in time and indefinitely long continuing

[4] having or feeling no doubt or uncertainty

[5] understood in a certain way

[6] not often

[8] block consisting of a thick piece of something

Down

[3] advanced in years

[7] information about recent and important events

[9] a very young mammal

[10] a written message addressed to a person or organization

Puzzle #19

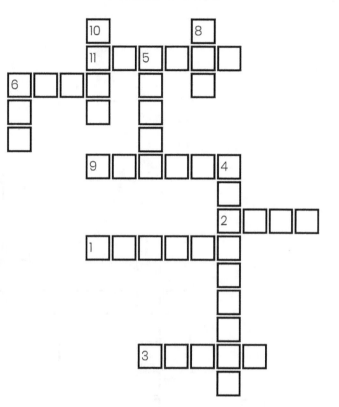

Across

[1] a mobile mass of muscular tissue located in the oral cavity

[2] cast off hair, skin, horn, or feathers

[3] name the letters that comprise the accepted form of

[6] a long rod of wood, metal, or plastic

[9] the process of taking in and expelling air during breathing

[11] with ease (`easy' is sometimes used informally for `easily')

Down

[4] a practitioner of homeopathy

[5] a person who is forcibly held in servitude

[6] dish baked in pastry-lined pan often with a pastry top

[8] affected by an impairment of normal physical or mental function

[10] require or want

Puzzle #20

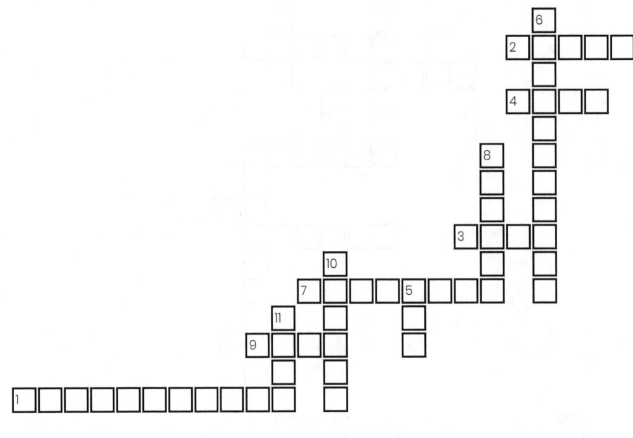

Across

[1] deriving from more than one source or style

[2] the state prevailing during the absence of war

[3] one side of one leaf of a book or other document

[4] a portable shelter

[7] ridicule with witty language used to convey insults or scorn

[9] the organic phenomenon that distinguishes living organisms

Down

[5] not treated with heat to prepare it for eating

[6] lacking protection or support

[8] a journey to some distant place

[10] equipment for taking photographs

[11] in a natural state

Puzzle #21

Across

[5] condemn or openly brand as disgraceful

[6] standardized procedure for measuring sensitivity or aptitude

[8] mix together different elements

Down

[1] an act that exploits or victimizes someone

[2] act of organizing and making ready for use or action

[3] something acquired without compensation

Puzzle #22

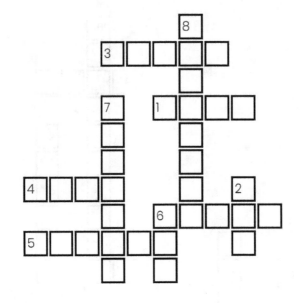

Across
[1] the cardinal number that is the sum of four and one

[3] destroy the integrity of

[4] having the necessary means or skill to do something

[5] ancient Greece

[6] set in motion, cause to start

Down
[2] a mixture of gases required for breathing

[6] a mountain or tall hill

[7] in whatever way or manner

[8] make as big or large as possible

Puzzle #23

Across

[1] cause fear in

[2] a representation of something, often on a smaller scale

[7] believe especially on uncertain or tentative grounds

[9] propel through the air

[11] bring under collective control

Down

[2] design or construct on a smaller scale

[3] detected or perceived via the auditory sense

[4] extensive tract of level open land

[5] changing back and forth between the chest voice and falsetto

[6] lying toward or situated in the west

[8] restore by replacing a part or putting together what is torn or broken

Puzzle #24

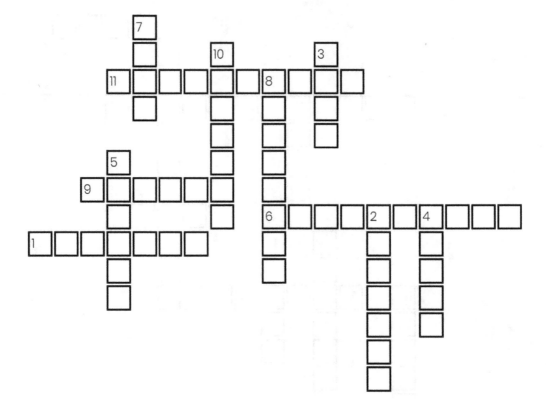

Across

[1] in some unspecified way or manner

[6] of or relating to commercial enterprise

[9] anything that belongs to a set or class

[11] 1st President of the United States

Down

[2] the physical position of something

[3] disposed of to a purchaser

[4] gossip passed around by word of mouth

[5] pick out or choose from a number of alternatives

[7] make a loud noise, as of an animal

[8] characterized by effort to the point of exhaustion

[10] a successful ending of a struggle or contest

Puzzle #25

Across

[4] the social process whereby cities grow

[8] making susceptible or sensitive to either physical or emotional stimuli

[10] a dwelling that serves as living quarters for a family

[11] with little or no delay

Down

[1] cause someone to suffer some adverse circumstance

[2] a quantity obtained by the addition of a group of numbers

[3] travel through water

[5] change direction with a swinging motion

[6] disposed to peace or of a peaceful nature

[7] sufficient for the purpose

[8] being certain that adverse effects will not be caused

Puzzle #26

Across
[2] make plain and comprehensible

[3] a hollow cylindrical shape

[8] strenuous effort

[10] distribute or disperse widely

Down
[1] having or showing belief in and reverence for a deity

[3] in contact with each other or in proximity

[4] devoid of or deficient in light or brightness

[5] a married woman

[7] at a distance in space or time

[9] hear with intention

[11] turned into ice

Puzzle #27

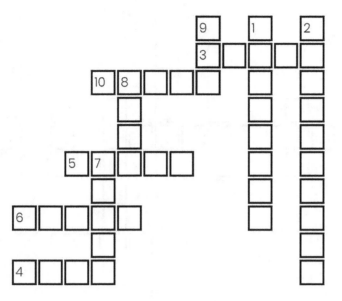

Across
[3] not affixed

[4] the general activity of selling

[5] happening at a time subsequent to a reference time

[6] a white crystalline carbohydrate used as a sweetener

[10] a human offspring (son or daughter) of any age

Down
[1] the day after today

[2] make ineffective by counterbalancing the effect of

[7] combustion of materials producing heat and light and smoke

[8] pursue for food or sport (as of wild animals)

[9] having lived for a long time or attained a specific age

Puzzle #28

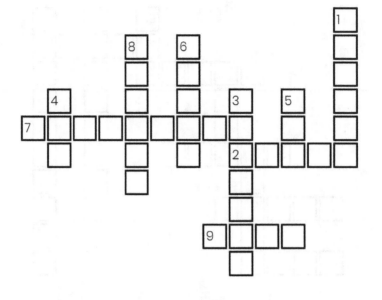

Across

[2] (of quantities) imprecise but fairly close to correct

[7] support, as through grants or other funds

[9] without any others being included or involved

Down

[1] a father or mother

[3] the act of departing

[4] an udder or breast or teat

[5] the cardinal number that is the sum of one and one

[6] the fundamental assumptions from which something is begun

[8] the second largest continent

Puzzle #29

Across

[1] shed tears because of sadness, rage, or pain

[4] basic and fundamental

[6] the state of being unsure of something

[8] the shore of a sea or ocean

[10] solid-hoofed herbivorous quadruped domesticated since prehistoric times

[11] warm-blooded egg-laying vertebrate with feathers and wings

Down

[2] for more time

[3] employ for a particular purpose

[5] a person who rescues you from harm or danger

[7] machine that creates mechanical energy and imparts movement

[9] not recognized

Puzzle #30

Across

[2] main or most important

[4] an ornamental coating to a building

[7] expect, believe, or suppose

[8] caught or fixed

Down

[1] a person whose occupation is instructing

[3] in part

[5] any of various small flat sweet cakes

[6] being the one previously mentioned or spoken of

[9] administer a sacrament signifying spiritual rebirth

Puzzle #31

Across

[1] a suite of rooms of a house divided into separate dwellings

[2] exercise power over in a cruel and autocratic manner

[5] wither, as with a loss of moisture

[9] separated or at a distance in place or position or time

[11] the taste experience when a savoury condiment is taken into the mouth

Down

[3] a human being

[4] a visual attribute of things from the light they emit

[6] synthetic material that can be molded into objects

[7] sharp curved horny process on the toe of some animals

[8] have its essential character

[10] the smallest continent

Puzzle #32

Across

[2] move so that an opening or passage is obstructed

[4] the act of swimming

[6] any of various fabrics (linen or cotton) used to make towels

[8] continue in a place, position, or situation

[11] something or someone that provides a source of happiness

Down

[1] perform vaccinations or inoculate against a disease

[3] the 5th letter of the Hebrew alphabet

[5] dish on which food is served or from which food is eaten

[7] apparel in general

[9] an unborn vertebrate in the later stages of development

[10] a living organism characterized by voluntary movement

Puzzle #33

Across
[2] set up or found

[3] change from governmental to private control or ownership

[4] take hold of so as to seize or stop the motion of

[5] give a character to relating to the profession of governing

[6] a visible clue that something has happened or is present

Down
[1] the activity of contributing to the fulfillment of a need

[5] to a distinctly greater extent or degree than is common

[7] the act of concentrating on something

[8] a very short time

[9] circulate or distribute or equip with

[11] a domestic fowl bred for flesh or eggs

Puzzle #34

Across

[4] capable of happening or existing

[5] gain knowledge or skills

[7] coming next after the first in position in space or time

[9] a mental image that is similar to optical perception

[11] a large body of salt water partially enclosed by land

Down

[1] an official who decides questions before a court

[2] a mechanical or electrical device that transmits energy

[3] a connected series of events or actions or developments

[6] descend freely under the influence of gravity

[8] a visual representation produced on a surface

[10] a tangible symbol signifying approval or distinction

Puzzle #35

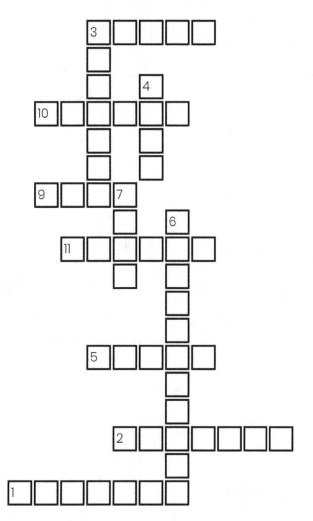

Across

[1] observe, check out, and look over carefully or inspect

[2] mythical creature with an eagle's head and a lion's body

[3] obstruct

[5] not correct

[9] a writer of verse

[10] a dark shape created by an object blocking a source of light

[11] marked by suitability or rightness or appropriateness

Down

[3] harmonious arrangement or relation of parts within a whole

[4] the middle of the day

[6] make personal or more personal

[7] the cardinal number that is the product of 10 and 100

Puzzle #36

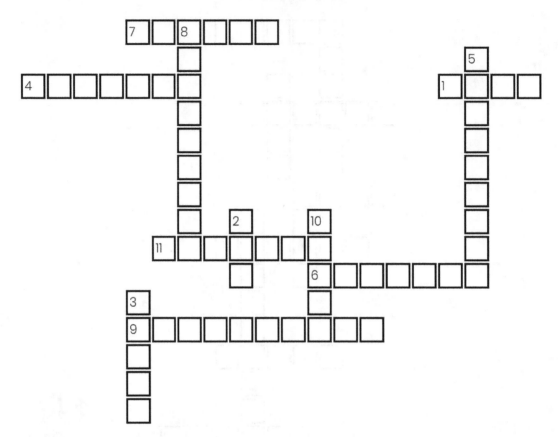

Across

[1] the hard fibrous lignified substance under the bark of trees

[4] cast or model anew

[6] occurring at the beginning

[7] advanced in complexity or elaboration

[9] of or relating to the treatment of bones or joints

[11] beat soundly

Down

[2] the collection of rules imposed by authority

[3] 16 ounces avoirdupois

[5] involving or characteristic of governing or social power

[8] stimulate (muscles) by administering a shock

[10] tested and proved to be reliable

Puzzle #37

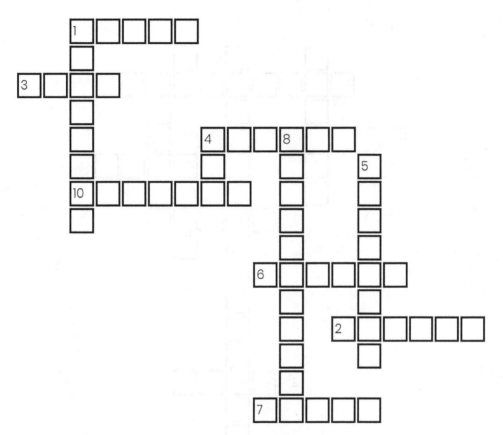

Across

[1] occasion on which people can assemble for social interaction

[2] the feeling aroused by something strange and surprising

[3] a thin pointed piece of metal that is hammered into materials as a fastener

[4] the significance of a story or event

[6] in the area or vicinity

[7] devote one's life or efforts to, as of countries or ideas

[10] put into a proper or systematic order

Down

[1] having existed from the beginning

[4] a segment of the trunk of a tree when stripped of branches

[5] the quality of being magnificent or grand

[8] happen at the same time

Puzzle #38

Across
[2] a line or route along which something travels or moves

[4] a characteristic state of feeling

[7] marked by suitability or rightness or appropriateness

[10] unusually great in amount or degree or extent or scope

[11] one thousandth (1/1,000) gram

Down
[1] dense coat of fine silky hairs on mammals

[3] the process of oxidizing

[4] come together

[6] in addition

[8] to a great degree

[9] the vital principle or animating force within living things

Puzzle #39

Across

[1] the main meal of the day served in the evening or at midday

[2] depression resulting from an undermining of your morale

[3] the vertical force exerted by a mass as a result of gravity

[8] move upward

[11] a series of moving pictures that tells a story

Down

[3] having intelligence and discernment

[4] a small part considered separately from the whole

[6] characterized by directness in manner or speech

[7] move forward by leaps and bounds

[9] a flat, usually green part of a plant attached to a stem

[10] an assembly to conduct judicial business

Puzzle #40

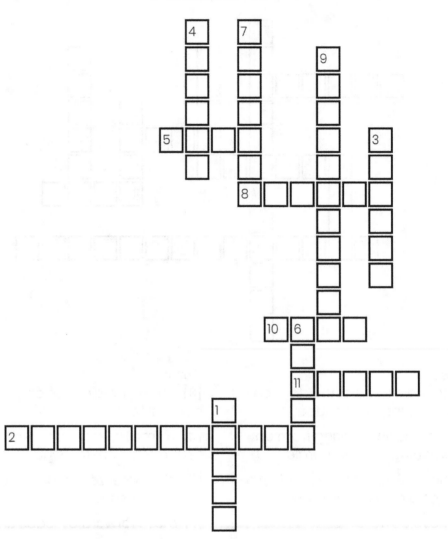

Across

[2] having both internal structure and external form of a crystal

[5] fail to keep or to maintain

[8] caused to fall to the ground

[10] at or toward an end or late period or stage of development

[11] come to pass

Down

[1] the time when something begins (especially life)

[3] a person who searches for something

[4] something having a similarity to something else

[6] stay away from

[7] being complete of its kind and without defect or blemish

[9] a process in which something passes to a different stage

Puzzle #41

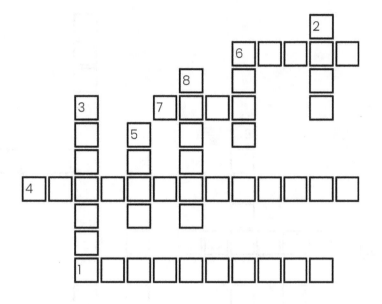

Across

[1] conforming with the principles or methods used in science

[4] the act of using technology to automate a process or system

[6] utter in a loud voice

[7] the mathematical symbol 0 denoting absence of quantity

Down

[2] the month following June and preceding August

[3] taxonomic group whose members can interbreed

[5] cause to move by pulling

[6] the act of firing a projectile

[8] a thin cylindrical pointed writing implement

Puzzle #42

Across
[1] a solid food prepared from the pressed curd of milk

[2] capable of happening or existing

[5] place a bet on

[7] a payment of part of a debt

[11] inside and toward a center

Down
[3] exceptionally bad or displeasing

[4] have the idea for

[6] belonging to one by birth

[8] a person who changes location

[9] being at or having a relatively great or specific elevation

[10] piece of timber or metal fixed firmly in an upright position

Puzzle #43

Across

[2] reduced to the simplest and most significant form possible

[8] the act of grinding to a powder or dust

[11] acknowledge faults or shortcomings or failing

Down

[1] of relatively small extent from one surface to the opposite

[2] in the interval

[3] the latter part of the day

[4] capital and largest city of Italy

[6] forward in time, order, or degree

[7] showing the wearing effects of overwork or care or suffering

[9] placing in medical care in a hospital

[10] less than normal in degree or

Puzzle #44

Across

[2] absolutely essential

[4] the action of destabilizing

[5] feelings of great warmth and intensity

[6] be at an angle

[10] deserving of esteem and respect

Down

[1] (KNO3) used especially as a fertilizer and explosive

[3] expel from a community or group

[5] administer a numbing or sleep-inducing drug to someone

[6] examine carefully for accuracy

Puzzle #45

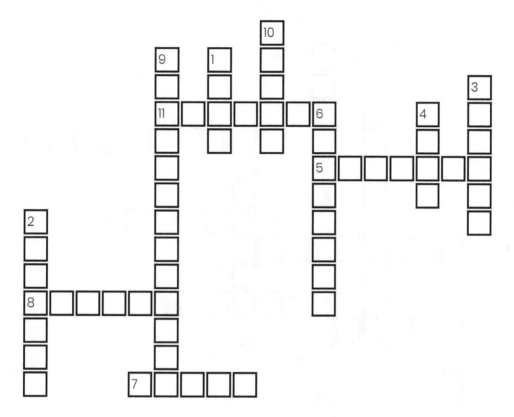

Across

[5] specify individually

[7] the state of being joined or united or linked

[8] a tangible and visible entity

[11] of or pertaining to China or its peoples or cultures

Down

[1] a vessel that carries passengers or freight

[2] be appropriate or necessary

[3] communication by word of mouth

[4] a set of garments for outerwear of the same fabric and color

[6] the cause of a disease

[9] the act of exploiting or unfairly treating someone

[10] characterized by an absence of agitation or activity

Puzzle #46

Across

[1] a unit of spoken language larger than a phoneme

[2] the land along the edge of a body of water

[3] having all necessary qualities

[5] a slight and usually refreshing wind

[6] having few parts

[9] a power to affect persons or events

Down

[3] in a close relation or position in time or space

[4] make free from bacteria

[5] actively or fully engaged or occupied

[7] characterized by denial or opposition or resistance

[11] destroy wantonly, as through acts of vandalism

Puzzle #47

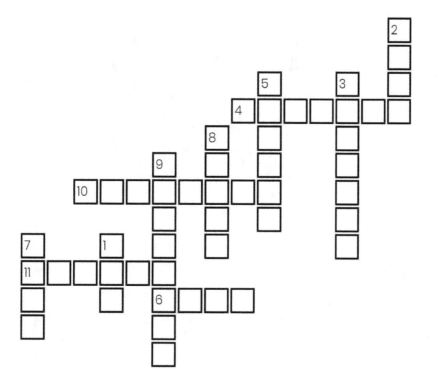

Across

[4] impart gradually

[6] a large piece of fabric used to propel a vessel

[10] raise to a more advanced stage of development

[11] come into possession of

Down

[1] utter aloud

[2] neither warm nor very cold

[3] a major road for any form of motor transport

[5] cry or whine with snuffling

[7] be priced at

[8] the text appearing in a book, newspaper, or other printed publication

[9] given official approval to act

Puzzle #48

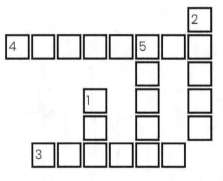

Across
[3] large or big relative to something else

[4] a military training exercise

Down
[1] above average in size or number or quantity

[2] a person who has achieved distinction in some field

[5] the quality that renders something desirable

Puzzle #49

Across

[2] a somatic sensation of acute discomfort

[3] a sheet of material that has been perforated with a pattern

[4] the act of providing a subsidy

[6] very light in color or highly diluted with white

[11] move fast by using one's feet

Down

[1] the act of starting something

[5] not violated or disregarded

[7] applying the mind to learning and understanding a subject

[8] at right angles to the plane of the horizon or a base line

[9] changing something from private to state control

[10] one or some or every or all without specification

Puzzle #50

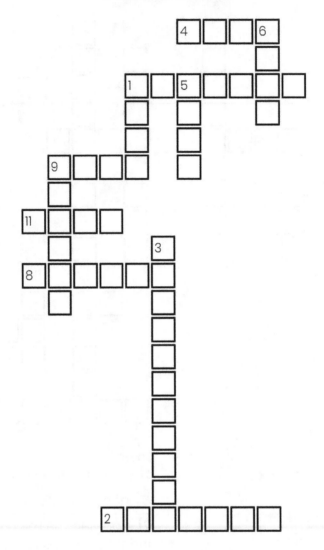

Across
[1] a republic in central Europe

[2] afflicted with or marked by anxious uneasiness or trouble

[4] having the most positive qualities

[8] securely in position

[9] in or at this place

[11] notify of danger, potential harm, or risk

Down
[1] transfer possession of something concrete or abstract

[3] one who commiserates with someone who has had misfortune

[5] any of many shrubs of the genus Rosa that bear roses

[6] a large number or amount

[9] the general condition of body and mind

Puzzle #51

Across

[1] the cardinal number that is the sum of six and one

[6] an instrument for measuring the distance between two points

[7] just preceding something else in time or order

[11] any distinct time period in a sequence of events

Down

[2] make sensitive or aware

[3] a series of steps to be carried out or goals to be achieved

[4] a group of soldiers

[5] an alloy of copper and zinc

[6] one of the large landmasses of the earth

[9] cause to move by pulling

[10] name the letters that comprise the accepted form of

Puzzle #52

Across

[2] temporary lodgings in the country for travelers

[6] the act of affirming or asserting something

[9] the act of assuming or maintaining a seated position

[11] attempt by employing effort

Down

[1] represented graphically by sketch or design or lines

[3] one of the twelve divisions of the calendar year

[4] the local environment

[5] the sound made by a dog

[7] an urban area with a fixed boundary that is smaller than a city

[8] put into service

[10] love unquestioningly and uncritically or to excess

Puzzle #53

Across

[1] do away with the military organization and potential of

[2] a piece of open land for recreational use in an urban area

[6] an item of information that is typical of a class or group

[7] turn up, loosen, or remove earth

[11] the father of your father or mother

Down

[2] the particular part of space occupied by something

[3] having a surface free from roughness or irregularities

[5] involving the mind or an intellectual process

[8] the creation of beautiful or significant things

[9] activities that are enjoyable or amusing

[10] an area that is in the middle of some larger region

Puzzle #54

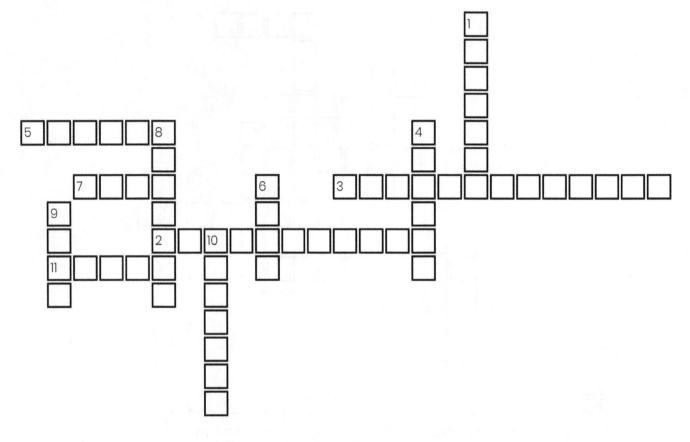

Across

[2] the degree of hotness or coldness of a body or environment

[3] the process by which an organism is preserved in rock

[5] a container that is usually woven and has handles

[7] (physics) a movement up and down or back and forth

[11] by chance

Down

[1] adorn or decorate with or as if with precious stones

[4] more quickly

[6] give a certain impression or have a certain outward aspect

[8] subjected to a physical treatment or action or agent

[9] move forward by leaps and bounds

[10] the act of creating something by casting it in a mold

Puzzle #55

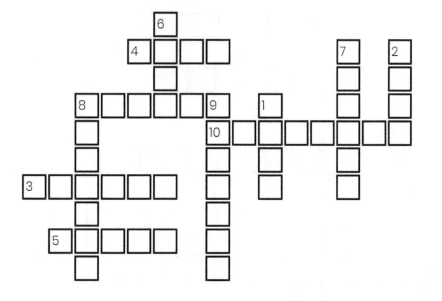

Across

[3] made afraid

[4] a young woman

[5] a representation of something, often on a smaller scale

[8] a phenomenon that is caused by some previous phenomenon

[10] a line of track providing a runway for wheels

Down

[1] an expression of some desire or inclination

[2] an unofficial association of people or groups

[6] the cardinal number that is the sum of eight and one

[7] pick out from a number of alternatives

[8] an imaginary line around the Earth forming a great circle

[9] vehicles or pedestrians traveling in a particular locality

Puzzle #56

Across

[4] marked by absence of sound

[5] five-toed pachyderm

[6] a series of steps to be carried out

[7] the flesh of animals used as food

[9] similar things placed in order or one after another

[11] bedding that keeps a person warm in bed

Down

[1] having color or a certain color

[2] the 2nd smallest continent

[3] assets belonging to an individual person or group

[8] the whole amount

[10] an outbuilding for housing automobiles

Puzzle #57

Across
[1] pleasing to the senses

[5] a seat for the rider of a horse or camel

[6] providing assistance or serving a useful function

[8] a medical science concerned with the spine and joints

[9] the front part of the human leg between the knee and the ankle

[11] two items of the same kind

Down
[2] not converted into ions·

[3] a fully developed person from maturity onward

[4] the posterior part of a human (or animal) body

[7] the activity of cherishing as divine

[10] praise formally and eloquently

Puzzle #58

Across

[1] an adornment made of precious metals and set with gems

[2] pleasing to the sense of taste

[5] convert to plant or animal remains

[6] in or near an inner area

[7] move or cause to move back and forth

[8] a limited period of time during which something lasts

[9] make repairs, renovations, revisions or adjustments to

Down

[3] a motor vehicle with four wheels

[4] a personal foe

[9] thorny shrub of a small tree having white to scarlet flowers

[10] of or relating to behaviorism

Puzzle #59

Across

[1] the content of observation or participation in an event

[2] cause to go somewhere

[5] attract strongly, as if with a magnet

[8] pay off a debt or obligation by making periodic payments

[10] of a light shade of red

[11] a unit of mass approximately equal to 0.035 ounces

Down

[3] incorporate within oneself

[4] an informal term for a father

[6] the use of speech for informal exchange of views or ideas

[7] a person who lives near another

[9] defying recognition as e.g. because of damage or alteration

Puzzle #60

Across

[1] preach the gospel to

[2] being or joined into a single entity

[3] act in a sentimental way or indulge in sentimental thoughts or expression

[4] spatially or metaphorically from a lower to a higher position

[11] unusual or striking

Down

[3] standing apart

[5] an itemized statement of money owed for goods or services

[6] make something seem more exciting or attractive than it is

[7] valuable timber tree of Panama

[8] the cardinal number that is the product of ten and three

[10] appoint as a substitute

Puzzle #61

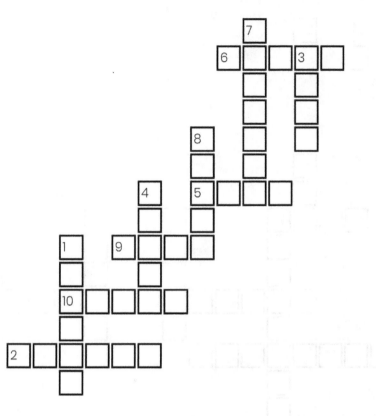

Across

[2] marked by extreme and violent energy

[5] acquire or deserve by one's efforts or actions

[6] the material that forms the hard outer covering of many animals

[9] water falling in drops from vapor in the atmosphere

[10] sound of any kind

Down

[1] domestic beast of burden descended from the African wild ass

[3] having the same or similar characteristics

[4] a collection of things sharing a common attribute

[7] a building where performances can be presented

[8] a large body of water that is part of the hydrosphere

Puzzle #62

Across

[1] the extent of a two-dimensional surface within a boundary

[2] not at all or in no way

[4] the content of cognition

[5] drawn or written with a pencil

[8] a native or naturalized member of a state

[11] of or relating to an organization

Down

[3] characterize as dangerous or wicked

[6] reducing the value of an asset over a period of years

[7] an established custom

[9] literature in metrical form

[10] a constitutional monarchy occupying the Japanese Archipelago

Puzzle #63

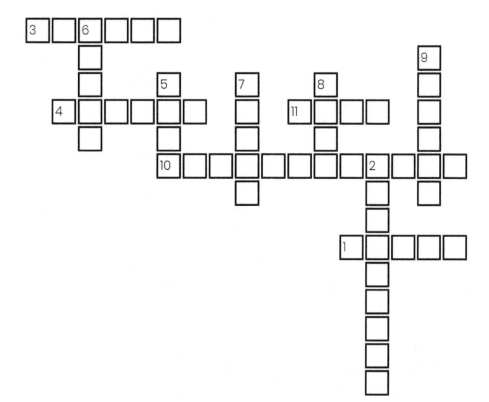

Across

[1] an abnormal new mass of tissue that serves no purpose

[3] of a color intermediate between red and blue

[4] made or consisting of or employing wood

[10] the earth science that studies fossil organisms

[11] having a low or inadequate temperature

Down

[2] make (a solid substance) liquid, as by heating

[5] having great spatial extension downward or inward

[6] excessive sternness

[7] acknowledged as a supposition

[8] quantifier meaning the greatest in number

[9] (postpositive) however

Puzzle #64

Across

[2] the way a person acts toward other people

[3] a perceptual structure

[4] male goat

[5] a beverage consisting of an infusion of ground coffee beans

[7] show unwillingness towards

[11] a man who plows

Down

[1] provoke the hostility of

[6] any period of seven consecutive days

[8] (of a nose) blocked

[9] cause to lose or change hue

[10] put into a certain place or abstract location

Puzzle #65

Across

[1] the imposition of standards or regulations

[2] broad in scope or content

[3] having strength or power greater than average or expected

[5] assign an initial value to a computer program

[8] in a state of sleep

[11] a club that is used as a weapon

Down

[4] an individual 3-dimensional object that has mass

[6] stress or single out as important

[7] depleted of energy, force, or strength

[9] the cardinal number that is the sum of one and one and one

[10] a condition in which an orderly system has been disrupted

Puzzle #66

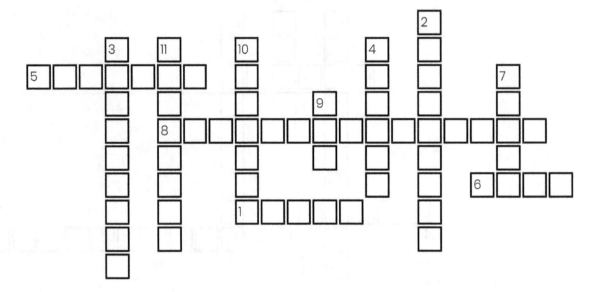

Across

[1] an indication that something has been present

[5] device allowing a swimmer to breathe while face down

[6] form a curve

[8] a performance given extempore without planning or preparation

Down

[2] definitely or positively

[3] put into a form intended for performance

[4] pertaining to living persons

[7] establish the validity of something

[9] a canine domesticated by man since prehistoric times

[10] make an effort

[11] a seeking for knowledge

Puzzle #67

Across
[2] yielding readily to pressure or weight

[4] eat human flesh

[7] higher in place or position

[11] a property that defines the individual nature of something

Down
[1] someone who attends the theater

[3] events that provide the generative force of something

[5] the ripened reproductive body of a seed plant

[6] the process of shedding tears

[8] lacking its natural or customary covering

[9] a visible suspension in the air of particles of a substance

[10] an informal term for a father

Puzzle #68

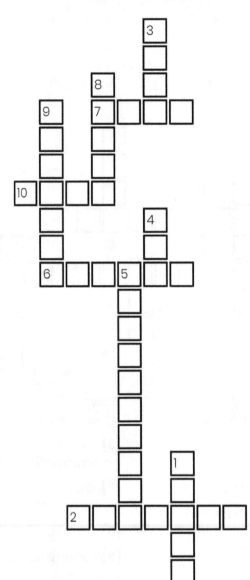

Across

[2] a compound of sulphur and some other element that is more electropositive

[6] easy to cut or chew

[7] a unit of language that native speakers can identify

[10] a database containing an ordered array of items

Down

[1] the sound made by the vibration of vocal folds

[3] having little money or few possessions

[4] water frozen in the solid state

[5] remove the entrails of

[8] having or denoting the characteristic taste of sugar

[9] belonging to times long past

Puzzle #69

Across
[1] the amount of money one makes over a period of time

Down
[2] the longest unit of geological time

[4] the act of bringing something

Puzzle #70

Across

[1] the act of penetrating or opening open with a sharp edge

[2] come or bring to an end

[5] meanness or nastiness

[8] the cognitive process whereby past experience is remembered

[10] two surfaces meeting at an angle different from 90 degrees

Down

[1] an institution of higher education

[3] a factual statement

[5] the atmosphere and outer space as viewed from the earth

[7] a metric unit of length equal to one thousandth of a meter

[9] make known

[11] a rectangular piece of absorbent cloth for drying or wiping

Puzzle #71

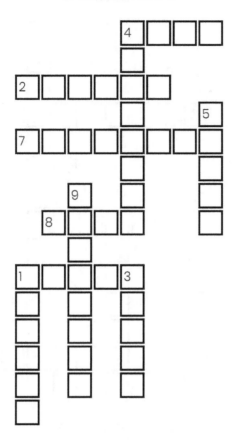

Across

[1] an ordered reference standard

[2] the act of working out the form of something

[4] so lacking in interest as to cause mental weariness

[7] what something is used for

[8] same in identity

Down

[1] a hand tool for lifting loose material

[3] holding or containing nothing

[4] put into a format that can be read or processed by computers

[5] below some quantity or limit

[9] direct the flow of

Puzzle #72

Across

[1] rescued

[2] any of various mostly cold-blooded aquatic vertebrates

[3] place into or assign to a class

[5] reach, make, or come to a conclusion about something

[8] watch attentively

[9] greater in size or amount or extent or degree

Down

[1] having vision, not blind

[4] having a high state of culture and social development

[6] action intended to nullify the effects of some action

[7] from a particular thing or place or position

[11] occupied or in the control of

Puzzle #73

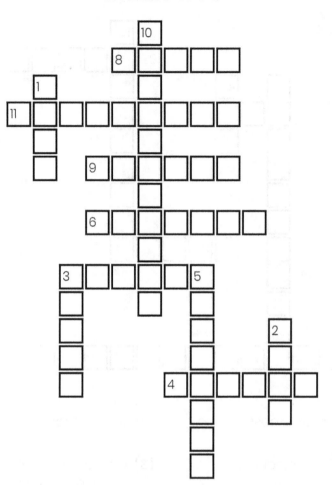

Across

[3] a natural body of water flowing on or under the earth

[4] grammatical number category referring to two or more items

[6] the weather in some location averaged over a period of time

[8] to the greatest degree or extent

[9] of the immediate past or just previous to the present time

[11] a line leading to a place or point

Down

[1] a piece of dishware normally used as a container for holding or serving food

[2] a series of steps to be carried out or goals to be achieved

[3] the place where some action occurs

[5] the act of representing something

[10] having a moustache

Puzzle #74

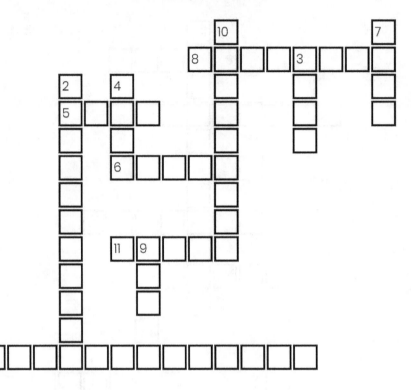

Across

[1] place special or excessive emphasis on

[5] the side of an object that is opposite its front

[6] the cardinal number that is the sum of seven and one

[8] pleasing in appearance

[11] possessing or displaying courage

Down

[2] the mother of your father or mother

[3] a cleansing agent made from the salts of vegetable or animal fats

[4] a quantity considered as a proportion of another quantity

[7] denote or connote

[9] an arrangement of objects or people side by side in a line

[10] make magnetic

Puzzle #75

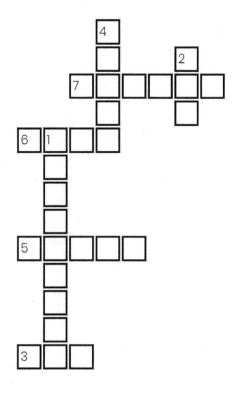

Across

[3] either extremity of something that has length

[5] rectangular block of clay baked by the sun or in a kiln

[6] the front of the human head from the forehead to the chin

[7] animal tissue consisting predominantly of contractile cells

Down

[1] the part of the day between noon and evening

[2] having lived for a long time or attained a specific age

[4] an established line of travel or access

Puzzle #76

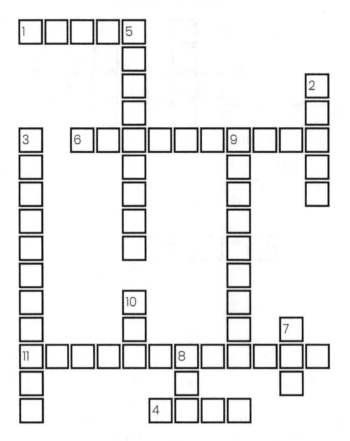

Across
[1] having the same or similar characteristics

[4] move by turning over or rotating

[6] a state in the western United States on the Pacific

[11] the act of making immune (especially by inoculation)

Down
[2] a path or track

[3] cause to form crystals or assume crystalline form

[5] very good

[7] having a high or higher than desirable temperature

[8] the facility where wild animals are housed for exhibition

[9] be a delegate or spokesperson for

[10] not subject to defeat

Puzzle #77

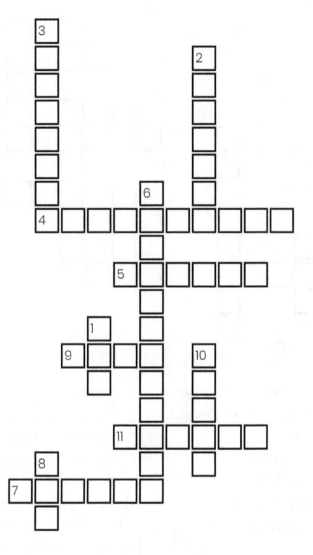

Across

[4] a relation between things or events

[5] a unit of time equal to 60 seconds or 1/60th of an hour

[7] the capital and largest city of England

[9] a set of two similar things considered as a unit

[11] the act of giving

Down

[1] an indentation of a shoreline smaller than a gulf

[2] make a proposal

[3] concerning an appreciation of beauty or good taste

[6] a medical specialist in the care of children

[8] move up and down repeatedly

[10] not soft or yielding to pressure

Puzzle #78

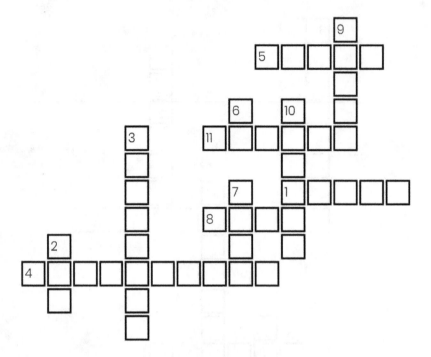

Across

[1] a structure taller than its diameter

[4] someone who assists or supports by giving a subsidy

[5] any piece of work that is undertaken or attempted

[8] utter a sudden loud cry

[11] farther along in space or time or degree

Down

[2] and nothing more

[3] a covering designed to be worn on a person's body

[6] have a specified quality or characteristic

[7] a body of (usually fresh) water surrounded by land

[9] having a circular shape

[10] with little weight or force

Puzzle #79

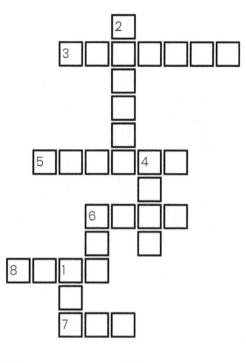

Across

[3] one of four equal parts

[5] in large part

[6] near in time or place or relationship

[7] the upper part of anything

[8] earlier than the present time

Down

[1] take a seat

[2] a device that attracts iron and produces lines of force

[4] weight to be borne or conveyed

[6] negation of a word or group of words

Puzzle #80

Across
[1] requiring or showing effort

[6] make objective or give reality to

[9] a toroidal shape

[11] a settlement smaller than a town

Down
[2] travel through water

[3] the act of limiting movement or making incapable of movement

[4] a prominent attribute or aspect of something

[5] a group of cattle or sheep or other domestic mammals

[7] a movable barrier in a fence or wall

[8] relating to the simplest units of an element or compound

[9] correspondence in the final sounds of two or more lines

Puzzle #81

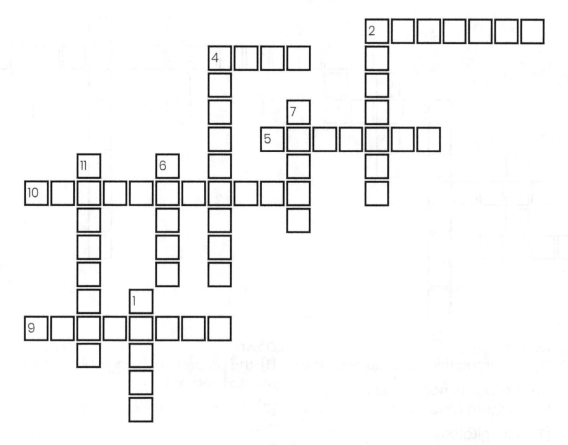

Across

[2] gather

[4] not moving quickly

[5] the territory occupied by a nation

[9] give a statement representing something

[10] put together out of artificial or natural components

Down

[1] logical or comprehensible arrangement of separate elements

[2] a large alphabetic character used in writing or printing

[4] a person with advanced knowledge of empirical fields

[6] marked by good fortune

[7] a songlike cry in which the voice fluctuates rapidly

[11] everything that exists anywhere

Puzzle #82

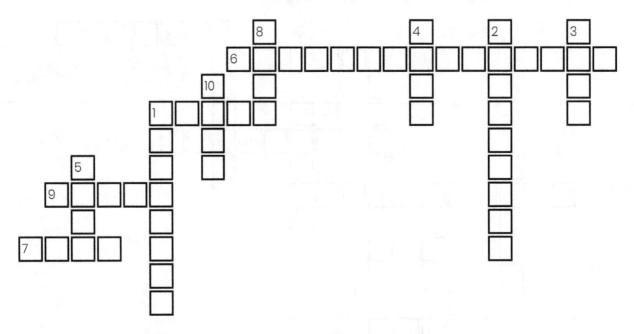

Across

[1] any broad thin expanse or surface

[6] the experience of becoming familiar with something

[7] not agitated

[9] influence that results in motion, stress, etc. when applied

Down

[1] the property of being physically or mentally powerful

[2] encouraging or approving or pleasing

[3] the pedal extremity of vertebrates other than human beings

[4] able to act at will

[5] a small replica of a person

[8] a piece of information about events that have occurred

[10] being the exact same one

Puzzle #83

Across

[1] a visual representation produced on a surface

[3] following the third position

[4] the side that is forward or prominent

[6] a person

[7] feeling or showing extreme displeasure or hostility

[11] draw a line or lines underneath to call attention to

Down

[2] the people of the Netherlands

[3] an examination administered at the end of an academic term

[5] an interval during which a recurring sequence occurs

[9] an angry dispute

[10] writing in a fictional form

Puzzle #84

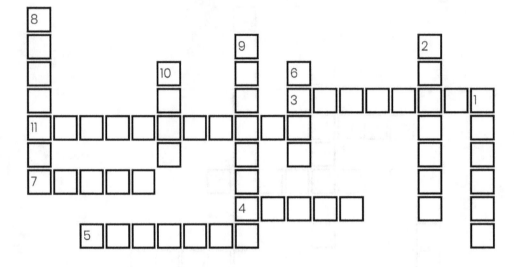

Across

[3] a fixed-wing aircraft powered by propellers or jets

[4] the time after sunset and before sunrise while it is dark outside

[5] the act of making a choice

[7] not thin

[11] making something plain or intelligible

Down

[1] motor that converts energy into work or motion

[2] covered with or as if with clothes or a wrap or cloak

[6] amounting to a large but indefinite number

[8] being complete of its kind and without defect or blemish

[9] creating or arousing uncontrolled emotion

[10] a coniferous tree

Puzzle #1

[1→] Clearly, [2↓] Trivialize, [3→] Sterilizer, [4↓] Gravel, [5↓] Fight, [6↓] Cipher, [7→] Bite, [8→] Jailed, [9→] Smoldering, [10↓] Enroll

Puzzle #2

[1↓] Hematology, [2→] Label, [3↓] Traumatize, [4↓] Cook, [5→] Bat, [6→] Read, [7→] Pediatrics, [8↓] Future, [9↓] Sell

Puzzle #3

[1→] Language, [2↓] Synthesize, [3↓] Know, [4↓] Fervor, [5→] Bring, [5↓] Build, [6↓] Simple, [7→] Remove, [8↓] Siphon, [8→] Sense, [9↓] Parallel

Puzzle #4

[1→] Monopolization, [2→] Behavioral, [3↓] Socialization, [4↓] Adventure, [5↓] Foreign, [6→] Require, [7↓] Bit, [7→] Born, [8→] Suddenly, [9→] Sleep, [11→] Attack

Puzzle #5

[1↓] Understanding, [2↓] Smell, [3→] Current, [4→] Movement, [5↓] Little, [6→] Plate, [7↓] May, [8→] Moving, [9↓] Putt, [9→] Practical, [11↓] Centiliter

Puzzle #6

[1→] Along, [2→] Smaller, [3↓] Skill, [4↓] Enjoy, [5↓] Propagandize, [5→] Pleasant, [6→] Polarize, [8↓] Hard, [9↓] Maximization, [10→] Aluminum, [11↓] Pen

Puzzle #7

[1→] Aggrandizement, [2↓] Courage, [3→] Prevent, [3↓] Pour, [4↓] Jet, [5↓] Root, [6↓] Toy, [7↓] Regular, [8→] Theorize, [10→] Continue, [11→] Mary

Puzzle #8

[1→] Changing, [2→] Centralized, [3↓] Careful, [4↓] Gain, [5↓] Reorganization, [6→] Refuel, [7→] Acclimatization, [8↓] Magnetized, [9↓] Plus, [9→] Produce, [10↓] Paul

Puzzle #9

[1↓] Valley, [2↓] Brush, [3→] Shine, [4↓] Fifty, [5↓] Cap, [6→] Organize, [7↓] Skin, [7→] Summer, [9→] Found, [10↓] Crenelate, [11→] Local

Puzzle #10

[1→] Similar, [2→] Sulfurous, [3↓] Include, [4↓] Jack, [5↓] Pencil, [6↓] Mars, [7↓] Ride, [8↓] Leukemia, [9→] Individualized, [10→] Motor, [11↓] Depth

Puzzle #11

[1→] Stone, [2↓] Bill, [3→] Frequently, [4→] Capitalize, [5→] Triangle, [6↓] Organization, [7↓] Writer, [8→] Branch, [9→] Generalization, [10↓] Happen, [11↓] Discuss

Puzzle #12

[1→] Affect, [2→] Offer, [3→] Indeed, [4↓] Multicolored, [5↓] Make, [6→] Jeweler, [7↓] Palace, [8↓] Circle, [9→] Heavy, [10↓] Patronize, [11→] Vocalization

Puzzle #13

[1→] Sound, [2→] Talk, [3↓] Bar, [4↓] Power, [5→] Short, [6↓] Flat, [7→] Caliber, [8↓] Tranquility, [9↓] Meter, [10↓] Studied, [11→] Introduce

Puzzle #14

[1↓] Identity, [2↓] Location, [3↓] Mustache, [4→] Stop, [5→] Particularize, [6↓] Port, [7↓] Cage, [8↓] Easy, [9↓] Right, [10→] Breathe, [11↓] Some

Puzzle #15

[1→] Grass, [2↓] Medicine, [3→] Fine, [4→] Watercolor, [5↓] Look, [6↓] Slip, [7↓] Pay, [8↓] Turn, [9→] Military, [10↓] Exclaim, [11→] Coat

Puzzle #16

[1↓] Reason, [2↓] Husband, [2→] Heading, [3→] Snow, [3↓] Stove, [5↓] Cozy, [5→] Cat, [6→] Sentence, [7↓] Plagiarize, [8→] January, [9↓] Truck

Puzzle #17

[1→] Nuts, [2↓] Reveler, [3↓] Becoming, [4→] Optimize, [5↓] Pasteurize, [6↓] Nod, [7→] Deal, [8↓] Folks, [9→] Knife, [10↓] Jar, [11→] Marshal

Puzzle #18

[1→] Glad, [2→] Constant, [3↓] Older, [4→] Sure, [5→] Taken, [6→] Seldom, [7↓] News, [8→] Slab, [9↓] Baby, [10↓] Letter

Puzzle #19

[1→] Tongue, [2→] Molt, [3→] Write, [4↓] Homeopath, [5↓] Slave, [6↓] Pie, [6→] Pole, [8↓] Ill, [9→] Breath, [10↓] Need, [11→] Easily

Puzzle #20

[1→] Bastardized, [2→] Peace, [3→] Page, [4→] Tent, [5↓] Raw, [6↓] Defenseless, [7→] Satirize, [8↓] Voyage, [9→] Life, [10↓] Camera, [11↓] Wild

Puzzle #21

[1↓] Using, [2↓] Mobilization, [3↓] Gift, [4↓] Symbol, [5→] Stigmatize, [6→] Test, [7↓] Enter, [8→] Mix, [9→] High, [10↓] Prioritize, [11→] Feel

Puzzle #22

[1→] Five, [2↓] Air, [3→] Break, [4→] Able, [5→] Greece, [6↓] Ben, [6→] Begin, [7↓] However, [8↓] Maximize

Puzzle #23

[1→] Frighten, [2→] Model, [2↓] Miniaturize, [3↓] Heard, [4↓] Field, [5↓] Yodeling, [6↓] Western, [7→] Hypothesize, [8↓] Fix, [9→] Throw, [11→] Collectivize

Puzzle #24

[1→] Somehow, [2↓] Setting, [3↓] Sold, [4↓] Rumor, [5↓] Select, [6→] Industrial, [7↓] Roar, [8↓] Grueling, [9→] Member, [10↓] Victory, [11→] Washington

Puzzle #25

[1↓] Victimize, [2↓] Sum, [3↓] Swim, [4→] Urbanization, [5↓] Swing, [6↓] Pacific, [7↓] Enough, [8↓] Safety, [8→] Sensitizing, [10→] House, [11→] Quickly

Puzzle #26

[1↓] Religious, [2→] Explain, [3↓] Together, [3→] Tube, [4↓] Dark, [5↓] Wife, [7↓] Away, [8→] Struggle, [9↓] Listen, [10→] Spread, [11↓] Frozen

Puzzle #27

[1↓] Tomorrow, [2↓] Neutralize, [3→] Loose, [4→] Sale, [5→] After, [6→] Sugar, [7↓] Flame, [8↓] Hunt, [9↓] Old, [10→] Child

Puzzle #28

[1↓] Parent, [2→] About, [3↓] Leaving, [4↓] Dug, [5↓] Two, [6↓] Basis, [7→] Subsidize, [8↓] Africa, [9→] Only

Puzzle #29

[1→] Cry, [2↓] Longer, [3↓] Apply, [4→] Essential, [5↓] Savior, [6→] Doubt, [7↓] Motor, [8→] Coast, [9↓] Unrecognized, [10→] Horse, [11→] Bird

Puzzle #30

[1↓] Teacher, [2→] Principal, [3↓] Partly, [4→] Facing, [5↓] Cooky, [6↓] Said, [7→] Guess, [8→] Stuck, [9↓] Baptize

Puzzle #31

[1→] Apartment, [2→] Tyrannize, [3↓] Person, [4↓] Color, [5→] Shrivel, [6↓] Plastic, [7↓] Claw, [8↓] Consist, [9→] Apart, [10↓] Australia, [11→] Flavor

Puzzle #32

[1↓] Immunize, [2→] Shut, [3↓] He, [4→] Swimming, [5↓] Plate, [6→] Toweling, [7↓] Clothes, [8→] Remain, [9↓] Fetus, [10↓] Animal, [11→] Pleasure

Puzzle #33

[1↓] Aid, [2→] Establish, [3→] Privatize, [4→] Catch, [5↓] Particularly, [5→] Politicize, [6→] Sign, [7↓] Attention, [8↓] Instant, [9↓] Supply, [11↓] Chicken

Puzzle #34

[1↓] Judge, [2↓] Machine, [3↓] Course, [4→] Possible, [5→] Learn, [6↓] Fall, [7→] Second, [8↓] Picture, [9→] Visualization, [10↓] Honor, [11→] Sea

Puzzle #35

[1→] Examine, [2→] Griffin, [3→] Block, [3↓] Balance, [4↓] Noon, [5→] Wrong, [6↓] Personalize, [7↓] Thou, [9→] Poet, [10→] Shadow, [11→] Proper

Puzzle #36

[1→] Wood, [2↓] Law, [3↓] Pound, [4→] Remodel, [5↓] Political, [6→] Initial, [7→] Higher, [8↓] Galvanize, [9→] Orthopedic, [10↓] Tried, [11→] Belabor

Puzzle #37

[1→] Party, [1↓] Primeval, [2→] Wonder, [3→] Nail, [4↓] Log, [4→] Lesson, [5↓] Splendor, [6→] Around, [7→] Serve, [8↓] Synchronize, [10→] Arrange

Puzzle #38

[1↓] Fur, [2→] Track, [3↓] Oxidization, [4→] Mood, [4↓] Meet, [6↓] Also, [7→] Proper, [8↓] Widely, [9↓] Spirit, [10→] Huge, [11→] Milligram

Puzzle #39

[1→] Dinner, [2→] Demoralization, [3↓] Wise, [3→] Weight, [4↓] Detail, [6↓] Frank, [7↓] Spring, [8→] Rise, [9↓] Leaf, [10↓] Court, [11→] Film

Puzzle #40

[1↓] Birth, [2→] Crystallized, [3↓] Hunter, [4↓] Analog, [5→] Lose, [6↓] Avoid, [7↓] Perfect, [8→] Thrown, [9↓] Development, [10→] Late, [11→] Occur

Puzzle #41

[1→] Scientific, [2↓] July, [3↓] Species, [4→] Mechanization, [5↓] Draw, [6↓] Shot, [6→] Shout, [7→] Zero, [8↓] Pencil

Puzzle #42

[1→] Cheese, [2→] Possible, [3↓] Terrible, [4↓] Conceptualize, [5→] Gage, [6↓] Native, [7→] Installment, [8↓] Traveler, [9↓] High, [10↓] Post, [11→] Interior

Puzzle #43

[1↓] Thin, [2→] Basic, [2↓] Between, [3↓] Evening, [4↓] Rome, [6↓] Forth, [7↓] Drawn, [8→] Pulverization, [9↓] Hospitalization, [10↓] Low, [11→] Apologize

Puzzle #44

[1↓] Saltpeter, [2→] Necessary, [3↓] Ostracize, [4→] Destabilization, [5↓] Anesthetize, [5→] Ardor, [6↓] Scrutinize, [6→] Slope, [8↓] Behind, [10→] Honorable, [11↓] Burn

Puzzle #45

[1↓] Ship, [2↓] Behoove, [3↓] Speech, [4↓] Suit, [5→] Itemize, [6↓] Etiology, [7→] Union, [8→] Object, [9↓] Victimization, [10↓] Quiet, [11→] Chinese

Puzzle #46

[1→] Syllable, [2→] Shore, [3→] Complete, [3↓] Closely, [4↓] Sterilize, [5↓] Busy, [5→] Breeze, [6→] Simple, [7↓] Negative, [9→] Influence, [11↓] Vandalize

Puzzle #47

[1↓] Say, [2↓] Cool, [3↓] Highway, [4→] Instill, [5↓] Snivel, [6→] Sail, [7↓] Cost, [8↓] Print, [9↓] Licensed, [10→] Civilize, [11→] Obtain

Puzzle #48

[1↓] Big, [2↓] Great, [3→] Bigger, [4→] Maneuver, [5↓] Value

Puzzle #49

[1↓] Beginning, [2→] Pain, [3→] Stencil, [4→] Subsidization, [5↓] Kept, [6→] Pale, [7↓] Study, [8↓] Vertical, [9↓] Nationalization, [10↓] Whatever, [11→] Run

Puzzle #50

[1↓] Give, [1→] Germany, [2→] Worried, [3↓] Sympathizer, [4→] Best, [5↓] Rose, [6↓] Tons, [8→] Steady, [9↓] Health, [9→] Here, [11→] Warn

Puzzle #51

[1→] Seven, [2↓] Sensitize, [3↓] Plan, [4↓] Troop, [5↓] Brass, [6→] Caliper, [6↓] Continent, [7→] Previous, [9↓] Draw, [10↓] Write, [11→] Stage

Puzzle #52

[1↓] Pictured, [2→] Camp, [3↓] Month, [4↓] Parts, [5↓] Bark, [6→] Statement, [7↓] Town, [8↓] Utilize, [9→] Sitting, [10↓] Idolize, [11→] Endeavor

Puzzle #53

[1→] Demilitarize, [2↓] Position, [2→] Park, [3↓] Smooth, [5↓] Mental, [6→] Instance, [7→] Dig, [8↓] Art, [9↓] Fun, [10↓] Center, [11→] Grandfather

Puzzle #54

[1↓] Bejewel, [2→] Temperature, [3→] Fossilization, [4↓] Faster, [5→] Basket, [6↓] Seem, [7→] Wave, [8↓] Treated, [9↓] Jump, [10↓] Molding, [11→] Maybe

Puzzle #55

[1↓] Wish, [2↓] Band, [3→] Scared, [4→] Girl, [5→] Model, [6↓] Nine, [7↓] Choose, [8↓] Equator, [8→] Effect, [9↓] Traffic, [10→] Railroad

Puzzle #56

[1↓] Colorful, [2↓] Europe, [3↓] Share, [4→] Silent, [5→] Elephant, [6→] Program, [7→] Meat, [8↓] Total, [9→] Series, [10↓] Garage, [11→] Blanket

Puzzle #57

[1→] Beautiful, [2↓] Unionized, [3↓] Adult, [4↓] Back, [5→] Saddle, [6→] Helpful, [7↓] Worship, [8→] Orthopedics, [9→] Shin, [10↓] Eulogize, [11→] Couple

Puzzle #58

[1→] Jewelry, [2→] Savory, [3↓] Automobile, [4↓] Enemy, [5→] Fossilize, [6→] Central, [7→] Shake, [8→] Term, [9↓] May, [9→] Modernize, [10↓] Behaviorist

Puzzle #59

[1→] Experience, [2→] Send, [3↓] Internalize, [4↓] Papa, [5→] Mesmerize, [6↓] Conversation, [7↓] Neighbor, [8→] Amortize, [9↓] Unrecognizable, [10→] Pink, [11→] Gram

Puzzle #60

[1→] Evangelize, [2→] United, [3↓] Separate, [3→] Sentimentalize, [4→] Upward, [5↓] Bill, [6↓] Glamorize, [7↓] Maria, [8↓] Thirty, [10↓] Deputize, [11→] Remarkable

Puzzle #61

[1↓] Donkey, [2→] Fierce, [3↓] Like, [4↓] Class, [5→] Earn, [6→] Shell, [7↓] Theater, [8↓] Ocean, [9→] Rain, [10→] Noise

Puzzle #62

[1→] Area, [2→] None, [3↓] Demonize, [4→] Idea, [5→] Penciled, [6↓] Amortization, [7↓] Habit, [8→] Citizen, [9↓] Poetry, [10↓] Japan, [11→] Organizational

Puzzle #63

[1→] Tumor, [2↓] Liquidize, [3→] Purple, [4→] Wooden, [5↓] Deep, [6↓] Rigor, [7↓] Given, [8↓] Most, [9↓] Though, [10→] Paleontology, [11→] Cold

Puzzle #64

[1↓] Antagonize, [2→] Behavior, [3→] Form, [4→] Billy, [5→] Coffee, [6↓] Week, [7→] Refuse, [8↓] Stopped, [9↓] Discolor, [10↓] Lay, [11→] Plowman

Puzzle #65

[1→] Normalization, [2→] Encyclopedic, [3→] Strong, [4↓] Body, [5→] Initialize, [6↓] Emphasize, [7↓] Spent, [8→] Asleep, [9↓] Three, [10↓] Disorganization, [11→] Cudgel

Puzzle #66

[1→] Trace, [2↓] Certainly, [3↓] Dramatize, [4↓] Living, [5→] Snorkel, [6→] Bend, [7↓] Prove, [8→] Extemporization, [9↓] Dog, [10↓] Attempt, [11↓] Research

Puzzle #67

[1↓] Theatergoer, [2→] Soft, [3↓] Cause, [4→] Cannibalize, [5↓] Fruit, [6↓] Tears, [7→] Upper, [8↓] Bare, [9↓] Vapor, [10↓] Dad, [11→] Character

Puzzle #68

[1↓] Voice, [2→] Sulfide, [3↓] Poor, [4↓] Ice, [5↓] Disembowel, [6→] Tender, [7→] Word, [8↓] Sweet, [9↓] Ancient, [10→] List

Puzzle #69

[1→] Income, [2↓] Eon, [3→] Anemia, [4↓] Internationalization, [4→] Importance, [5→] Worse, [6↓] Hat, [7↓] Event, [8↓] Stem, [10→] Cavil, [11↓] Differ

Puzzle #70

[1↓] College, [1→] Cutting, [2→] Finish, [3↓] Truth, [5→] Spite, [5↓] Sky, [7↓] Millimeter, [8→] Memory, [9↓] Announce, [10→] Bevel, [11↓] Towel

Puzzle #71

[1↓] Shovel, [1→] Scale, [2→] Design, [3↓] Empty, [4↓] Digitize, [4→] Dull, [5↓] Under, [7→] Function, [8→] Same, [9↓] Canalize

Puzzle #72

[1→] Saved, [1↓] Seeing, [2→] Fish, [3→] Categorize, [4↓] Civilized, [5→] Decide, [6↓] Neutralization, [7↓] Off, [8→] Observe, [9→] More, [11↓] Held

Puzzle #73

[1↓] Dish, [2↓] Plan, [3↓] Scene, [3→] Stream, [4→] Plural, [5↓] Modeling, [6→] Climate, [8→] Fully, [9→] Recent, [10↓] Mustachioed, [11→] Direction

Puzzle #74

[1→] Overemphasize, [2↓] Grandmother, [3↓] Soap, [4↓] Rate, [5→] Rear, [6→] Eight, [7↓] Mean, [8→] Handsome, [9↓] Row, [10↓] Magnetize, [11→] Brave

Puzzle #75

[1↓] Afternoon, [2↓] Old, [3→] End, [4↓] Route, [5→] Brick, [6→] Face, [7→] Muscle

Puzzle #76

[1→] Alike, [2↓] Trail, [3↓] Crystallize, [4→] Roll, [5↓] Excellent, [6→] California, [7↓] Hot, [8↓] Zoo, [9↓] Represent, [10↓] Won, [11→] Immunization

Puzzle #77

[1↓] Bay, [2↓] Suggest, [3↓] Esthetic, [4→] Connection, [5→] Minute, [6↓] Pediatrician, [7→] London, [8↓] Bob, [9→] Pair, [10↓] Solid, [11→] Giving

Puzzle #78

[1→] Tower, [2↓] But, [3↓] Clothing, [4→] Subsidizer, [5→] Labor, [6↓] Be, [7↓] Lake, [8→] Call, [9↓] Round, [10↓] Softly, [11→] Beyond

Puzzle #79

[1↓] Sit, [2↓] Magnet, [3→] Quarter, [4↓] Load, [5→] Mostly, [6↓] Not, [6→] Near, [7→] Top, [8→] Past

Puzzle #80

[1→] Labored, [2↓] Swim, [3↓] Immobilization, [4↓] Feature, [5↓] Herd, [6→] Externalize, [7↓] Gate, [8↓] Molecular, [9→] Ring, [9↓] Rhyme, [11→] Village

Puzzle #81

[1↓] Order, [2→] Collect, [2↓] Capital, [4→] Slow, [4↓] Scientist, [5→] Country, [6↓] Happy, [7↓] Yodel, [9→] Describe, [10→] Manufacture, [11↓] Universe

Puzzle #82

[1→] Sheet, [1↓] Strength, [2↓] Favorable, [3↓] Foot, [4↓] Free, [5↓] Doll, [6→] Familiarization, [7→] Calm, [8↓] Fact, [9→] Force, [10↓] Very

Puzzle #83

[1→] Image, [2↓] Dutch, [3↓] Final, [3→] Fourth, [4→] Front, [5↓] Rhythm, [6→] Human, [7→] Angry, [9↓] Quarrel, [10↓] Fictionalization, [11→] Underline

Puzzle #84

[1↓] Engine, [2↓] Wrapped, [3→] Airplane, [4→] Night, [5→] Willing, [6↓] Many, [7→] Thick, [8↓] Perfect, [9↓] Exciting, [10↓] Pine, [11→] Explanation

CPSIA information can be obtained
at www.ICGtesting.com
Printed in the USA
LVHW060232130723
752367LV00024BA/433